POP PROMPTS
FOR SWIFTIES

99 WRITING PROMPTS

By Erik Patterson

Camden High Street Books
2023

Pop Prompts For Swifties: 99 Writing Prompts
Copyright © 2023 Erik Patterson

Print ISBN: 979-8-9878016-1-1
eBook ISBN: 979-8-9878016-2-8
Library of Congress Control Number: 2023902395
First Paperback Edition, March 2023

Cover design by Hannah Alpert
Copy editing by Sherry Angel
Printed in the United States of America
Los Angeles, CA

www.erikpatterson.org

This book is meant for educational, scholarship, and research purposes. By taking a critical look at the themes in Taylor Swift's work, we aim to inspire writers to create their own unique works of personal writing and fiction. Writers using this book are encouraged to research their own hearts and psyches in order to become scholars of their inner selves. Song titles are referenced in the spirit of Fair Use and readers should seek out and purchase Taylor Swift's music on their own as a supplement to the original writing prompts in this book. Taylor Swift has no involvement with this book. The use of her name is merely descriptive and should not be interpreted as a sign of endorsement.

Praise for
Pop Prompts For Swifties: 99 Writing Prompts

"If only this book were around when I was getting ready to write *my* book. Erik is the writing docent in your museum of stories and ideas. Read this book and let him help you gather your thoughts and get your mind moving."

—Retta, author of *So Close to Being the Sh*t,
Y'all Don't Even Know*

"Every life is flush with meaningful experiences, and man is it nice to have someone help us excavate them to create. Erik's prompts pick up right where each of Taylor's songs leave off—now it's your turn!"

—Drew Seeley, actor, singer, songwriter

"Turn to any page in *Pop Prompts*, set your timer, and write. Settling in and writing without a plan, I mean truly letting your mind go like Erik advises, is the closest you'll come to God (whether or not you believe)."

—Andrea Askowitz, author of *My Miserable, Lonely,
Lesbian Pregnancy*

"I loved flipping through to my fave Swift songs and getting creatively inspired by the suggestions of how to loosen up my own writing. Whether it's to explore things in your work-in-progress, kick loose stuff in your personal life, or use in a classroom as a warm-up exercise, Erik's playlist prompts help to elevate your writing game."

—Cecil Castellucci, author of *Shifting Earth*

CONTENTS

ALBUM: Speak Now

ALBUM: 1989

INTRODUCTION

I was late to the Taylor Swift party. Of course, I knew some of her songs. I danced to "Shake It Off" at several wedding receptions. I saw the music video for "You Belong With Me" and enjoyed the wordplay. I sang along to "Look What You Made Me Do" in my car. But I was only a casual fan.

Then suddenly we were all stuck at home during the pandemic. Like a lot of us, I was alone and depressed. I didn't feel creative. The writing wasn't flowing like it normally does.

And that's when *Folklore* came out. I was struck by Taylor's vulnerability, I was drawn in by her honest lyrics, I was carried away by her catchy melodies. I must have listened to that album at least a million times. I felt like Taylor "got" me, and I finally understood her.

So I listened to her other albums. I watched all her videos. I read fan theories about the hidden meanings behind her lyrics. Whether or not these hidden meanings are true, one thing is very clear: SWIFTIES ARE THE MOST CREATIVE PEOPLE EVER.

And now I was one of them! But even better, I was writing again. It was like I was living through my own movie montage, the one where the writer gets their groove back, and my soundtrack was Taylor Swift's entire discography.

In this book of writing prompts, we'll use Taylor's music as a source of inspiration. Let her music be your muse. Her songs can help you find your own voice.

Whether you're jotting down your thoughts in a journal or you're a published author looking for a way to shake up your writing routine, or anywhere in between, *Pop Prompts For Swifties* is for you.

Even if you aren't a die-hard Swiftie, don't despair. You are among the lucky ones who get to discover Taylor's music while getting into a writing groove. But you don't even have to think of yourself as a writer to do these writing prompts. Anyone can use them as a tool for self-expression and reflection.

First thoughts are often your best thoughts, so use the journal pages in this book to get those down. Write in the blank space between the lines. If you want to write more, you can dig even deeper in another stand-alone journal.

Inspiration is only a song away. Just put on your favorite Taylor Swift album, pick a prompt, and start writing!

POP PROMPTS
FOR SWIFTIES
99 WRITING PROMPTS

TIM MCGRAW

Think of someone from your past. Someone you loved. Someone you wish you hadn't lost touch with. What do you remember most fondly about them?

Write a letter to them that they're never going to read.

Tell them what you were afraid to say when you had the chance.

When you close your eyes and think of them, what are they wearing?

What do you miss about them?

What did they teach you?

What do you hope they remember most fondly about you?

Write.

FIRST THOUGHTS

PICTURE TO BURN

Think of a person in your past you ended up hating.

Make a list of reasons you despise them. Burn your memories of them to the ground.

Is there anything else you DON'T miss about them?

What memory of them do you MOST wish you could forget?

Why can't you?

Write.

FIRST THOUGHTS

TEARDROPS ON MY GUITAR

Make a list of metaphors to describe someone you have a crush on. (It can be a romantic crush, a friend crush, or a talent crush.)

If they were an emotion, what would it be?

If they were a place, where would they be?

If they were a food, what would they taste like?

If they were architecture, what kind of building would they be?

If they were a guitar, what kind of music would they play?

If they were a weather pattern, what would they look like?

Write.

FIRST THOUGHTS

A PLACE IN THIS WORLD

Where do you feel like you fit in?

Sometimes it takes a while to find our "people." The people who accept us with all our foibles, who love our eccentricities, who are there for us no matter what. Our community. Our "found" family.

How did you find your found family? How did you first connect with them?

How do they enrich your life? How do they make you feel like you have a "place" in the world?

You might still be looking for them. That's okay. If that's the case, envision a place where you feel safe and happy.

What is it about this place that makes it special for you?

Write.

FIRST THOUGHTS

COLD AS YOU

Who's the coldest person you know?

Has this person ever done you dirty?

What did they take from you?

Be specific.

Imagine this person is sitting across from you right now. What do you want to say to them?

Don't hold back. Make them feel how they hurt you.

Demand an apology.

Write.

FIRST THOUGHTS

THE OUTSIDE

What could you do to become the best version of yourself?

It doesn't matter how old we are, we always have new things we can learn. Think of at least three things you haven't figured out about yourself yet . . .

If you had to do a research paper and you were the subject, where would you start your investigation?

If you got a report card for the way you live your life, what grades would you get?

Where do you feel above average?

What parts of your life feel stuck in the middle?

And where do you have room for improvement?

Write.

FIRST THOUGHTS

TIED TOGETHER WITH A SMILE

Look at yourself in the mirror.

Who do you see staring back at you?

What does that person dislike about themselves?

What is that person afraid of?

If that person asked you to cheer them up, what would you tell them?

What makes that person in the mirror smile?

Write.

FIRST THOUGHTS

STAY BEAUTIFUL

Try to remember a day or a night or a moment that felt perfect.

Close your eyes and visualize that day, or night, or moment as clearly as you possibly can.

Take pictures of that moment in your mind's eye.

Then open your eyes and describe these pictures.

Be as detailed as you possibly can. Find moments of everyday beauty.

Try to describe at least seven pictures of this day, or night, or moment.

Write.

FIRST THOUGHTS

SHOULD'VE SAID NO

Think of a time when someone close to you did the wrong thing.

What did they do wrong?

What was the fallout of their actions?

How would you have done things differently? Start a sentence with "they should've . . ." and start another sentence with "I would've . . ."

If you could change the outcome now, would you?

Write.

FIRST THOUGHTS

MARY'S SONG (OH MY MY MY)

Who do you want to be when you're eighty-seven years old?

Write a vision of this future you. (NOTE: Current eighty-seven-year-olds can pick any future age they want to envision. Shoot for three digits!)

What is eighty-seven-year-old you proud of?

What does eighty-seven-year-old you regret?

What does eighty-seven-year-old you love to do?

What does eighty-seven-year-old you wish present-day you knew about yourself?

Write.

FIRST THOUGHTS

OUR SONG

Write down the name of someone you love.

This can be a romantic love, a platonic love, a familial love. It can be a fleeting love, an eternal love, an unrequited love, a love that burned brightly, a love that fizzled out, a love you wish had lasted longer, a secret love.

Any kind of love!

Just pick a person who adds meaning to your life.

If they were a song, which one would they be?

What genre of music do they feel like?

Are they a whisper or a shout?

If they had a theme song, what would the lyrics be?

What instrument is most like them?

What tempo do they live in?

Describe the musicality of your relationship.

Write.

FIRST THOUGHTS

I'M ONLY ME WHEN I'M WITH YOU

How do you see yourself reflected in the people you're closest to?

Who makes you feel your truest self?

What do you have in common with this person?

What are your shared passions?

What parts of your personality do they wake up?

Is there a part of you that no one knows but them?

Write.

FIRST THOUGHTS

INVISIBLE

Have you ever been someone's second choice?

Or worse, maybe they didn't even know you were an option. Maybe you were completely invisible to them.

We've all gone through rejection. Have you ever wished you could go back and plead your case again? Maybe they didn't SEE you before. Maybe if you said the right thing you could help them see who you really are.

Make a list of your best qualities that might not be immediately apparent to others.

What are your hidden strengths?

Be persuasive. Why should we be LUCKY to know you?

Write.

FIRST THOUGHTS

A PERFECTLY GOOD HEART

Do you have any scars?

Let's start with the scars people can see. Take an inventory of the scars—big and small—on your body. How and when did you get each of these perfect imperfections?

Once you've gone through the scars on the outside look at any scars you might have on the inside.

What are the stories behind these inner wounds?

Choose one and think about how you can help it heal.

Write.

FIRST THOUGHTS

FEARLESS

What is your greatest fear?

Face that fear right now.

When and how was it born?

What does it keep saying to you?

Talk back.

Feel your strength.

Be fearless.

Write.

FIRST THOUGHTS

FIFTEEN

What's the worst lie you ever believed?

Who told you this lie?

Why did you believe them?

How did it feel when you discovered the truth?

Write.

FIRST THOUGHTS

LOVE STORY

If you could be a character from your favorite story, who would you be?

What do you love about this character?

Why do you identify with them?

How are the two of you similar?

How are you different?

What could you learn from this character?

How would you behave differently if you were this character?

Write.

FIRST THOUGHTS

HEY STEPHEN

Let's think about missed opportunities.

Have you ever had the chance to tell someone how you felt about them . . . but you didn't say it?

This might be an unrequited love.

Or maybe you didn't stand up to a boss or a bully.

If you could go back, what would you tell this person?

Pretend they're walking away and you want to get their attention. You yell out "hey" followed by their name. They turn and give you a look, like, *yeah*? You can take it from there . . .

Write.

FIRST THOUGHTS

WHITE HORSE

Have you ever been your own hero?

When we're in trouble, we can't always expect someone to come rescue us on some metaphorical white horse.

We've gotta watch out for ourselves. We must be our own heroes.

So.

When have you saved yourself?

How did you do it?

How did you feel afterwards?

Write.

FIRST THOUGHTS

YOU BELONG WITH ME

Convince someone to choose you.

Think of something very specific that you want.

It could be a relationship (but it doesn't have to be a romantic one) . . .

It could be someone you want to collaborate with on an artistic project . . .

It might be a boss you want to impress . . .

No matter who you choose, start with the phrase "I belong with you." Then make the best argument you possible can.

Write.

FIRST THOUGHTS

BREATHE

Before you start writing, take a breath.

I mean it. Take a deep breath.

Breathe in. Breathe out. Relax your shoulders. Let go of any tension you don't realize you're holding onto.

Now think of a friend who's no longer around.

Someone you never got to say goodbye to.

Say goodbye to them now.

Tell them everything they meant to you.

The good, the bad, the complicated. All of it.

Write.

FIRST THOUGHTS

TELL ME WHY

Who are you mad at right now?

Tell them why.

Don't hold anything back.

UNLEASH YOUR ANGER.

Make it achingly clear what this person has done wrong.

Be painfully honest about how they've hurt you.

Ask them why.

Write.

FIRST THOUGHTS

YOU'RE NOT SORRY

Make a list of apologies you're owed.

I'm talking overdue apologies.

Choose one apology that should have come a lonnggggg time ago.

Maybe this person never learned, maybe they're never gonna change. Deep down, you know you're never going to get the apology you want.

So stop letting it eat at you.

Write how you WISH things had gone. What you WANTED them to say. What you HOPED they would have learned.

Then let it go.

Write.

FIRST THOUGHTS

THE WAY I LOVED YOU

Think about something specific you need to hear right now.

Who do you need to hear it from?

Imagine they're talking to you right now, giving you . . .

. . . the best compliment
. . . the most reassuring promise
. . . a genuine apology

How would that conversation go?

Write.

FIRST THOUGHTS

FOREVER & ALWAYS

What's the worst betrayal you've ever experienced?

Was it a complete shock, or did you see it coming?

Some of the relationships we think are going to last forever secretly have expiration dates. What do you think about this person's duplicity now?

Are you grateful they aren't an "always" in your life, or does their deception still sting?

How did it forever change you?

Write.

FIRST THOUGHTS

THE BEST DAY

Make a list of qualities you love about someone who helped make you the person you are today.

Who had the most influence on you when you were growing up?

Think of someone who raised you. It doesn't have to be a parent. There are a ton of people you might write about: a sibling, a grandparent, a teacher, a favorite aunt or uncle, a friend. Make it someone you've always looked up to.

Think about the impact this person has had on your life.

What parts of yourself feel most like them?

What was the best day you ever spent with them?

Write.

FIRST THOUGHTS

CHANGE

Do you know who the next "you" is?

We're constantly changing. The person you were ten years ago might not even recognize who you are today.

So what do you want your next incarnation to look like?

Think about all the ways in which you would like to change.

But think about it as more than just a change. Think of it as a transformation. An evolution. A rebirth.

Who do you want to become?

Write.

FIRST THOUGHTS

JUMP THEN FALL

How good are you at taking risks?

Do you jump headfirst into scary situations? Or do you tiptoe forward?

Think of something scary you need to do.

Then think of the boldest, bravest person you know.

How would they approach this scary situation?

Write.

FIRST THOUGHTS

UNTOUCHABLE

Have you ever suffered from an unrequited love?

What did it feel like?

How did you handle this romantic imbalance?

Think of a metaphor to describe the distance you felt from this person.

What made them so untouchable?

Have you moved on?

If not, why not?

What can you do to help yourself let go?

Write.

FIRST THOUGHTS

COME IN WITH THE RAIN

What do you want more than anything in the world?

Do you have any friends who can help you get it? Imagine you're talking to them right now.

Make an argument for why you need it. No, "need" isn't a strong enough word. Why do you DESERVE to have it?

Convince your friend.

Be bold. Be cocky. Be undeniable.

Write.

FIRST THOUGHTS

SUPERSTAR

Who's your celebrity crush?

Why are they the superstar of your heart? Seriously, why do you like them so much? Go deeper than looks.

How have they inspired you?

If you could talk to them, what would you say?

What would you want them to say back?

Write.

FIRST THOUGHTS

THE OTHER SIDE OF THE DOOR

Think of a time when you pushed someone away.

A time when you were afraid to express how you really felt.

A time when you didn't let yourself be vulnerable.

Tap into that vulnerability now.

Imagine they're just on the other side of a door and you can tell them anything you desire.

What are you going to say to them?

Write.

FIRST THOUGHTS

YOU ALL OVER ME

What was the last lie you told?

What would have happened if you'd told the truth? How would things be different now?

Now think of a lie you told in the past and ask yourself these same questions.

What purpose did this lie serve?

If you had a do-over, would you tell the lie again? Or would you tell the truth this time?

Write.

FIRST THOUGHTS

MR. PERFECTLY FINE

How many distinct personalities do you have within you?

Think about all the different "faces" you show the world.

When does each face come out?

How does each face serve you?

Which face do you wear most often?

Which face is closest to who you really are?

Write.

FIRST THOUGHTS

WE WERE HAPPY

What's your happiest memory?

Who were you with?

Why does this memory stay with you?

How did this specific happiness feel?

Close your eyes and take a moment to really remember it. Then recreate this memory as best you can.

What can you learn from this moment of happiness?

Write.

FIRST THOUGHTS

THAT'S WHEN

What are you waiting for?

That isn't a rhetorical question. I really mean it: WHAT in your life are you waiting for? Maybe you're waiting for lots of things?

Make a list of everything you're waiting for, big or small.

Then slowly work through your list, looking at each thing one by one, and . . .

. . . instead of asking "WHEN is this going to happen?" ask yourself, "HOW can I make this happen?"

Write.

FIRST THOUGHTS

DON'T YOU

What are your personal dealbreakers?

Knowing what you don't want can be as important as knowing what you want.

So brainstorm at least twenty things you DO NOT want . . .

. . . in a romantic relationship.

. . . in your career.

. . . in your future.

. . . in a Friday night out on the town.

. . . in a friendship.

Et cetera.

Write.

FIRST THOUGHTS

BYE BYE BABY

Say goodbye to a bad habit.

What (or who) do you need to purge from your life?

Make a list of all the reasons this habit isn't healthy.

Then say goodbye to this habit.

Like, literally say goodbye to it. Write it a letter. Tell it why you're done! Let it know, in no uncertain terms, never to come crawling back to you. Tell it to eff off, if you have to. Just make sure this habit knows you're done with it for good.

Write.

FIRST THOUGHTS

MINE

Think back on a "first" from your past. Any first.

What do you remember about this first time?

What were your expectations?

Did it meet those expectations? Was it better? Worse?

Write an ode to this first experience.

Write about all the ways this "first" feels like it's yours, and yours alone.

Write.

FIRST THOUGHTS

SPARKS FLY

How does a crush feel different from love?

Okay, first: how does a crush feel?
What does a crush sound like? What does it look like? What does it smell like? And what does it taste like?

Now: how does love feel?
Go through all the senses again—but go deeper with them this time.

How many ways can you describe love without using the word "love."

Make us feel the sparks fly.

Write.

FIRST THOUGHTS

BACK TO DECEMBER

Who do you owe an apology to?

Tell them how you did them wrong.

Swallow your pride and admit it was your fault.

Be an open wound.

Ask for forgiveness.

Tell them what they mean to you.

Set a timer for 13 minutes.

Write.

FIRST THOUGHTS

SPEAK NOW

What's the boldest thing you've ever done?

What were the ramifications of your daring act?

As the old saying goes, fortune favors the bold. So how did your courageousness favor you?

Take a moment to celebrate your audaciousness.

Write an ode to your fearlessness.

Be as bold in your words as you were in your valiant act.

As Taylor wrote in the liner notes to this song, "you always regret what you don't say." So speak now.

Write.

FIRST THOUGHTS

DEAR JOHN

Have you ever ghosted anyone?

Sometimes the best way to get out of a bad relationship is to skip the goodbye. The other person doesn't always need, or deserve, a reason. We usually think of ghosting as taking the easy way out— and it's true: ghosting can definitely be a cowardly thing to do.

But what if ghosting is the best way to show yourself grace?

So . . . let's rephrase the original question: have you ever had a good ghosting?

If you had to end the relationship all over again, would you still ghost them?

Did you learn anything from the end of this relationship?

Write.

FIRST THOUGHTS

MEAN

What's the most awful thing anyone's ever said to you?

Don't relive this emotional trauma—this is your chance to expel it.

Let go of those cruel words. Don't let the person who said them define you.

Tell them why they're wrong. But do it in the kindest way possible.

Think of your words as a gift. You're helping a bully understand their actions. You're teaching them how to be a better person.

Write.

FIRST THOUGHTS

THE STORY OF US

have you ever experienced a happy Accident?

write about a moment when you just happened to be in the right place at the right time and your Life is the better for it.

how has chance Informed your life Story?

One day in the future, when you look at your life Now, what serendipity will you see?

write.

FIRST THOUGHTS

NEVER GROW UP

What parts of your childhood made you who you are today?

What was the most important thing that happened in your first year of life? (Obviously you can't remember your first year of life, but what do you know from pictures and stories?)

What was the most important thing that happened in your second year of life? (Same note as above.)

What was the most important thing that happened in . . .

. . . your third year of life?

. . . your fourth year of life?

. . . your fifth year of life?

Go through your life, year by year, until you get to today. One moment from each year.

Write.

FIRST THOUGHTS

ENCHANTED

If you were granted the ability to cast one magical spell, what would you do with this power?

Think big.

You can do anything.

Visualize what the world might look like the day after you perform your spell.

And the week after . . .

And a year after . . .

How much change can you bring about with just one spell or wish?

Write.

FIRST THOUGHTS

BETTER THAN REVENGE

Think of someone who hurt you.

They say thriving is the best revenge—so how is your life better than theirs?

What are they missing out on?

What do you wish you could teach them?

Is there any way to heal your relationship?

If they apologized, what would they have to say to make things right?

Write.

FIRST THOUGHTS

INNOCENT

What's your biggest regret?

Wouldn't it be nice to be able to change the past?

Since we can't do that, let's do the next best thing: ask yourself what lessons you can take from this regret you feel.

Take a big, hard look at it.

Because we CAN change the future by learning from the past.

So what do you want to do differently?

How can you turn this thing you regret into something positive?

Write.

FIRST THOUGHTS

HAUNTED

Think of someone who used to be important to you who's faded into the past.

For whatever reason, you just aren't close to this person anymore. Maybe the relationship ran its course.

What pieces of this relationship do you still hold onto?

What parts of this person or relationship still haunt you?

How does this make you feel?

What can you do about it?

Write.

FIRST THOUGHTS

LAST KISS

Make a list of important kisses.

Your favorite first kiss.

Your saddest last kiss.

Your most surprising kiss.

Your worst kiss.

A kiss you really didn't want.

A kiss you hoped for that never happened.

A kiss that wasn't as good as you fantasized.

Your longest kiss.

All the kisses! As many significant kisses as you can think of!

After you've made your list, choose one kiss to write about in detail. What did this kiss mean to you?

Write.

FIRST THOUGHTS

LONG LIVE

Take a few minutes to scroll through some of the older photos in your phone.

Find a photo that has a lot of energy in it.

Put yourself back in that moment.

What do you want to remember about that day?

Or, more importantly, what do you want to NEVER FORGET?

Imagine you're telling the story of that day to a friend who wasn't there. Don't leave out any details. Try to bring that photograph back to life with your words.

Write.

FIRST THOUGHTS

OURS

What do others judge about you?

It may be something about your appearance, or something you like to do that they don't approve of.

Whatever it is, reclaim it.

Talk back to the haters.

Tell them why they're wrong.

Write.

FIRST THOUGHTS

IF THIS WAS A MOVIE

What's your favorite movie cliche?

If your life was a movie, how would it be different?

If your life was a movie, what would it be rated?

If your life was a movie, what would be the biggest recurring theme?

If your life was a movie, who would be the main supporting characters?

Now imagine your life is a movie and write an exciting, dramatic, fun scene that hasn't happened yet.

Write.

FIRST THOUGHTS

SUPERMAN

What is your greatest fantasy?

We all daydream about things we think would make us happy, even if they might not ever come true. Sometimes just dreaming about them is enough.

So . . .

Do some daydreaming now.

Dream BIG.

Don't limit yourself to the constraints of reality.

ANYTHING can happen in this reality you're about to create. As long as it's wonderful. As long as it makes you happy.

Write.

FIRST THOUGHTS

STATE OF GRACE

What's the most surprising thing that's ever happened to you?

Something completely unexpected.

It can be a good surprise or a bad surprise—in fact, do the prompt twice, once for a joyous surprise and once for a sad one.

How did the surprising nature of this event make it feel more unique or memorable?

Write.

FIRST THOUGHTS

RED

Make a list of colors and jot down a few adjectives to describe what each color means to you.

When do you feel orange?

Have you ever had a yellow day?

What puts you in the mood for green?

How do you get yourself out of blue?

Who's the most indigo person you know?

When are you in the mood for violet?

And what makes you see red?

Write.

FIRST THOUGHTS

TREACHEROUS

What was your last worst decision?

How long did it take you to realize you were doing the wrong thing?

Were you able to get out of it?

What were the repercussions of your bad choice?

If you could have a do-over, what decision would you make?

How do you hope things will go the second time around?

Write.

FIRST THOUGHTS

I KNEW YOU WERE TROUBLE

What's the best mistake you've ever made?

Maybe it taught you something important about yourself.

Maybe you did something wrong that helped you see the right thing to do.

Maybe your mistake gave you a chance to deepen a relationship?

Whatever you did, you found a way to make the best of the situation.

How the hell did you do that?

Explore the ways you turned this mistake into something to celebrate.

Write.

FIRST THOUGHTS

ALL TOO WELL

Listen, this writing prompt is all about that scarf. We can't ignore the scarf.

What's YOUR version of Taylor Swift's lost scarf?

Visualize all the clothes in your closet. Pick an item of clothing that has emotional weight. Don't think of it like *baggage*. It's more like this item of clothing carries *stories* inside it.

Tell one of those stories right now.

What does this item of clothing symbolize in the story?

How does this item of clothing make you feel?

If this item of clothing could speak, what would it say?

Go to a coffee shop, get yourself a maple latte, and write.

FIRST THOUGHTS

22

Tonight feels like a perfect night for . . .

What do you like to do for fun?

Imagine you're about to have an unforgettable night. The most amazing night ever!

What does this night look like?

Don't limit yourself to reality. If you want to include literal magic in your fantasy of a perfect night, go for it.

Write.

FIRST THOUGHTS

I ALMOST DO

Is there anyone you SHOULDN'T ever get back in touch with?

Maybe you know it wouldn't be healthy to talk to them. Maybe you know you need to move on. Maybe they've already moved on and you know you should respect that.

Whatever your reason, you know you shouldn't reach out.

Tell them everything you want to say here.

Write this instead of calling.

FIRST THOUGHTS

WE ARE NEVER EVER GETTING BACK TOGETHER

What's the story behind your last breakup?

When did you know it was the end?

Was it an easy breakup? A terrible one? Did things linger in some sort of undefined space before you ended it for good? Or was it a clean break?

Make a list of all the reasons that relationship had to end. What's the best one and why?

Write.

FIRST THOUGHTS

STAY STAY STAY

Who is the kindest person you know?

What do they fear, fear, fear?

What do they hope, hope, hope?

What do they dream, dream, dream?

That's three fears, three hopes, and three dreams!

If you don't know, use your imagination. (But call them later and find out.)

Write.

FIRST THOUGHTS

THE LAST TIME

What have you done once that you never want to do again?

What did you learn the first time?

Remind yourself why you feel so strongly about this.

If you have more than one "never," do this prompt for each of them.

Be strong. Stand your ground.

Think of this as a personal mission statement.

"I'm never going to _____ again because _____."

Write.

FIRST THOUGHTS

HOLY GROUND

If you could relive one day from your past, what day would you choose?

Relive that day right now.

Jot down as much as you can remember.

Think of it as a series of moments.

Remember the details:
What were you wearing?
What did you have for breakfast that day?
What was the weather like?
Who were you with?
What did you talk about?

Why did you choose this day?

Does anything about this day feel holy?

Write.

FIRST THOUGHTS

SAD BEAUTIFUL TRAGIC

They say your struggles make you stronger.

Think of a moment from your past that was exceptionally difficult. Can you look back and find a reason to be grateful for this trial?

You walked through a fire and came out the other side.

Can you find any beauty in the darkness?

Write.

FIRST THOUGHTS

THE LUCKY ONE

"I'm one of the lucky ones. Things just always seem to go my way."

Close your eyes and say it aloud, even if you don't believe it.

Say it a few times. Say it until the words feel right in your mouth.

Then make an argument defending that statement.

Why are you so lucky?

How has luck impacted your life?

What's the luckiest thing that ever happened to you?

How have you created your own luck?

Write.

FIRST THOUGHTS

EVERYTHING HAS CHANGED

Who do you wish you were closer to?

It must be someone you personally know, but otherwise it could be anyone: a friend, an acquaintance, a partner, a parent.

How can you change your relationship with them for the better?

Come up with at least 22 questions to ask them.

Make them meaty questions. Nothing they could give a yes or no answer to.

What do you want to know about them?

Write.

FIRST THOUGHTS

STARLIGHT

Is there anything you want to accomplish that feels like an impossible dream?

Why does it seem unrealistic to you?

What if it *isn't* impossible?

Imagine how it would feel to make this dream come true. Really put yourself in that headspace.

Then brainstorm everything you would have to do to make this dream a reality.

Write.

FIRST THOUGHTS

BEGIN AGAIN

Is there anything you want to reclaim?

Maybe your last relationship wasn't that great—how do you want to begin your next one?

Maybe your last job sucked—what job do you hope to begin soon?

Maybe the place where you live doesn't feel like a home—where do you want to make a new beginning?

Think of all the ways you'd like to begin again.

Write.

FIRST THOUGHTS

THE MOMENT I KNEW

Allow yourself to mourn a promise unfulfilled.

Think about the hope of a promise given, and your anticipation of a promise fulfilled.

Relive the slow realization that your trust and faith has been broken—the disappointment, the feeling of regret in your gut, the wish that things had gone differently.

Describe the moment you knew they weren't going to come through for you.

Have you let go?

Have you moved on?

Write.

FIRST THOUGHTS

COME BACK . . . BE HERE

Who do you yearn for?

What do you think they're doing right now?

Visualize a normal day in their life.

Now visualize that same day . . . but include yourself in the daydream.

What do you see the two of you doing together?

Be in the moment with them.

Write.

FIRST THOUGHTS

GIRL AT HOME

What's the best "no" you've ever given?

Is there a "no" you're especially proud of?

A "no" that was hard fought. A difficult "no." A "no" that you were nervous about. A "no" that required a lot of strength. A "no" that you felt from the bottom of your soul.

Feel free to write about multiple times you've said "no."

Your best "no!" Your second best "no!" Your third best "no!"

Do you have a "no" that deserves an honorable mention? Shout out to that "no" now!

What's the most important thing you know about saying "no"?

Write.

FIRST THOUGHTS

BETTER MAN

Think of a moment of bravery from your past.

How did you do it?

Where did you find the strength?

Imagine you're teaching a class on bravery and you're using this moment as an example: can you analyze your own strength?

Was it a moment of fearlessness? Or was the moment full of fear that you were able to overcome? Or did this moment exist somewhere in between fearlessness and terror?

Take us through your thought process.

Teach us how to be better at facing our fears.

Write.

FIRST THOUGHTS

NOTHING NEW

The more we know, the less we know.

Isn't that one of the greatest ironies of aging? Don't you wish you still knew everything like you used to?

Write about how your worldview has changed as you've gotten older.

Pick a year from your past. Any year.

What did you hope for? What did you dream about? What did you know with certainty?

Now answer those same questions today.

What do you hope for? What do you dream about? What do you know with certainty?

How do your answers differ?

Write.

FIRST THOUGHTS

BABE

Okay, it's secret time.

Not your secret. A secret that belongs to someone else.

What's the biggest secret you know?

How much power does this secret hold?

When you heard this secret, how did it change your relationship with the secret holder?

Write.

FIRST THOUGHTS

MESSAGE IN A BOTTLE

Do you have a secret?

What would happen if this secret came out?

Would it really be all that bad? How would you get through it?

Is there someone you confide in? Maybe this book can be your message in a bottle. A place where you can write the secret down just to see how it feels. A place where you can practice getting it out. A place where you can get closer to being free of the burden of this thing that's eating away at you.

Try it.

Confess your secret.

Write.

FIRST THOUGHTS

I BET YOU THINK ABOUT ME

Let's get petty.

Who do you have a competitive relationship with?

How are you better than them?

Go ahead and gloat.

Celebrate all the ways you've won.

When they think about you, what makes them jealous?

Write.

FIRST THOUGHTS

FOREVER WINTER

What are you struggling with right now?

Get it off your chest.
It's okay. You're not alone.
This too shall pass.
Winter never lasts forever. Eventually it transitions into spring.

Put your struggle into words.
Be patient with yourself. Try to show yourself some grace.

Practice how you might talk to a friend about your pain.

Write.

FIRST THOUGHTS

RUN

Do you ever feel like running away?

When we hear the words "run away," we usually think of running away FROM something. But let's think of this differently: where do you want to run away TO?

Something better.
Something sweeter.
Something hopeful.

What does this place look like?

Write.

FIRST THOUGHTS

THE VERY FIRST NIGHT

Go back in time to the beginning of an important relationship.

How did you meet?

What's your earliest memory with them? (Make up what you don't remember.)

Did you have any idea then how important they would be to you now?

What was your very first night with them like?

Write.

FIRST THOUGHTS

WELCOME TO NEW YORK

Have you ever been CHANGED by a city?

How did it get under your skin?

Can you pinpoint the moment when you first realized this city held a piece of your heart?

Write a love letter to this city. Things to include:

- A food you love to eat here.
- A friend you met here.
- How you get around in this city.
- Your favorite building.
- An interesting fact about the city's history.
- A mystery about this city.
- Three songs you would put on the city's soundtrack.
- Three smells of the city.
- Three sounds of the city.
- A color you associate with this city.
- If this city could speak, what would it say?

Write.

FIRST THOUGHTS

BLANK SPACE

What (or who) makes you burn with jealousy?

If you let yourself succumb to jealousy, it'll eat away at your insides. If you let it go unchecked, it'll grow and grow. So, instead of letting it fester in some dark corner of your brain, purge yourself of all your jealous feelings now.

Where does this jealousy come from?

Look at your own life and ask yourself what's missing. What blank space does this jealousy occupy?

How can you make this blank space feel vibrant and colorful?

Write.

FIRST THOUGHTS

STYLE

If you could come of age in a different era, what decade would you choose?

Why do you feel connected to this time?

What do you like about the styles of this era?

Think of a significant historical event from these years and imagine how you would have reacted to it in real time.

How would you be different now if you had been part of that historical event?

Write.

FIRST THOUGHTS

OUT OF THE WOODS

What's the best reconciliation you've ever experienced?

Every fight is followed by a moment of making up. (Hopefully!)
So . . .

Think of a big fight you had with a partner, friend, or family
member.

How did the fight end?
Who said sorry first?
How did you makeup?
Is your relationship out of the woods now?

Write.

FIRST THOUGHTS

ALL YOU HAD TO DO WAS STAY

Who's the last person you want to hear from right now?

Imagine your phone is ringing.
You look at the caller ID.
IT'S THEM.

You decide to answer the phone.
You're going to tell them how you feel.

Start with: "All you had to do was . . ."

How do you want this conversation to go?

Write.

FIRST THOUGHTS

SHAKE IT OFF

Compliment yourself.

I mean it. Give yourself a compliment that reflects the real you.

Now another one.

And another one.

Come up with as many compliments for yourself as you possibly can.

I MEAN IT! If you don't have at least ten compliments on your list, you're not trying hard enough.

No one else is going to read this, so feel free to be vain. Really pump yourself up.

Shake those bad feelings off with this list of good ones.

Write.

FIRST THOUGHTS

I WISH YOU WOULD

Do this prompt at 2 a.m.

Think of someone you miss.

Write down the words, "I wish you would . . ."

And then complete that sentence as many times as you possibly can.

When you think you've come up with all the things you wish they would do . . . think a little harder. Come up with five more woulds you wish they'd do.

Write.

FIRST THOUGHTS

BAD BLOOD

Who do you have bad blood with?

Take a moment to remember the good times:
How did you first connect with this person?
What did you love about them?
Why was your bond so strong?

Now look at the not-so-good times:
When did things start to sour?
What do you think of this person now?
How did it feel when your bond broke?

Is there any way the two of you might mend things in the future?

Write.

FIRST THOUGHTS

WILDEST DREAMS

Who's your favorite ex?

Compose an email or a note to them. (You don't have to send it. Think of this as a secret conversation.)

Describe the best day you had with them.

Tell them three things you admired about them.

Then tell them three things you hope they admired about you. (Why not? It's YOUR writing prompt!)

What is the wildest thing you could say to them?

Tell them how you want them to remember you.

Write.

FIRST THOUGHTS

HOW YOU GET THE GIRL

What's an unsolved mystery in your life that you can't stop thinking about?

It could be as small as "where did my favorite shirt disappear to" or as big as "why did so-and-so ghost me?"

Whatever the mystery, it should be something that weighs on you.

Think of it as your own personal Stonehenge, your own personal Amelia Earheart, your own personal Who Shot JFK?

What might the answer to your mystery be? Come up with a theory.

Write.

FIRST THOUGHTS

THIS LOVE

THiNK OF SOMEONE FROM YOUR PAST WHO LEFT A PERMANENT MARK ON YOU.

HOW DID THIS PERSON cHANGE YOU?

WHAT DID YOU LEArN FROM THEM? iT COULD Be A GOOd LESSON OR A BAD LESSON.

whAT WOULD YOUR LiFE lOOK LIKe NOW IF YOU'D NEVER MET THEM?

wHAT DOES THIS LOVE YOU HAVE FOr THEM LOOK LiKE?

WHAt WiLL YOU nEVER gEt OVER ABOUT ThEM?

WRiTE THIs WITH LOVE.

FIRST THOUGHTS

I KNOW PLACES

Are you a hunter or a fox?

You can interpret that however you'd like to.

Alternate ways to look at it:
Are you a right or a left?
Are you a yin or a yang?
Are you a top or a bottom?
Are you paper or plastic?
Are you take-out or dine-in?

Whatever dichotomy you decide on, pick a side. Then analyze why you feel this way.

Write.

FIRST THOUGHTS

CLEAN

Are you someone who defines yourself by who you're with?

You are a wonderful, whole, unique individual. Wash yourself
clean of this other person and write about what makes you *you*.

Where did you begin your story?
Who are you known by? Who are you not known by?
Who do you love recklessly?
When did you pay the price for your actions?
Who do you dance to forget?
Whose house have you driven by at night?
Who are your friends and who are your enemies?
Who do you only see in your dreams?
Who do you want to come back someday?
When was timing a funny thing?
When did everyone watch you?
Has losing someone else ever helped you find yourself?

Write.

FIRST THOUGHTS

WONDERLAND

What are you curious about?

What do you wonder?

What makes absolutely no sense to you?

Who do you NOT understand?

When have you asked yourself, "What's that about?" And WHAT WAS IT ABOUT?

It's time to vocalize all the questions you've ever been afraid to ask. Don't hold back. There are no stupid questions.

Write.

FIRST THOUGHTS

YOU ARE IN LOVE

How does your favorite couple make it work?

Let's think about the love that's all around us.

What does love look like from the outside?

Pick a couple you admire. Then act like you're a sociologist and study them.

How do they show their love to each other?
Do you know what their love languages are?
How do they complement each other?

What can you learn about love from them?

Write.

FIRST THOUGHTS

NEW ROMANTICS

What's your personal definition of romance?

Write a romantic manifesto.

You can use examples you've experienced.

You can use favorite examples from popular culture.

You can use your imagination. (If you're creating a fictional romance, make up a character whose initials are JJ, LT, TL, JM, JG, HS, CH, or JA.)

Lay out your vision for what romance should look like.

Make us swoon!

Write.

FIRST THOUGHTS

ABOUT THE AUTHOR

Erik Patterson is an award-winning screenwriter, playwright, and writing teacher.

His play, *One of the Nice Ones*, earned the Los Angeles Drama Critics Circle Award. His theater work has been produced or developed by Playwrights' Arena, the Los Angeles Theatre Centre, Theatre of NOTE, the Evidence Room, The Actors' Gang, the Echo Theater Company, the Lark Play Development Center, Moving Arts, Black Dahlia, Naked Angels, the Mark Taper Forum, and New Group. His plays have been nominated for the Ovation Award, the Stage Raw Award, the LA Weekly Award, and the GLAAD Media Award.

His writing for TV has been recognized with the Humanitas Prize and the Writer's Guild Award, as well as two Emmy nominations. Along with his writing partner, Jessica Scott, Erik has written films for Warner Bros., Universal, 20th Century Fox, Disney, Freeform, MTV, Paramount, Hallmark, and Syfy, among others. Film and TV credits include: *Abandoned* (starring Emma Roberts and Michael Shannon), *R.L. Stine's The Haunting Hour*, *Another Cinderella Story* (starring Selena Gomez and Jane Lynch), *Deep Blue Sea 2*, *Radio Rebel*, and many more.

Erik is a graduate of Occidental College and the British American Drama Academy. He has developed a wealth of writing prompts through online "Sunday Sprints" that attract writers seeking community and inspiration to do their best work.

www.erikpatterson.org

Books by Erik Patterson

Pop Prompts: 200 Writing Prompts Inspired by Popular Music
Available in paperback and e-book

Pop Prompts is a collection of writing prompts that will help you dig deeper and break through creative blocks. Each prompt is paired with a pop song. Let the music be your muse as you work on your memoir, novel, script, poem—or even your own songs. This book can also be a daily jumpstart for therapeutic journaling. Use it however you want, whenever you want. As long as you're writing you're doing it right.

Praise for *Pop Prompts: 200 Writing Prompts Inspired By Popular Music*

"The hardest thing to find as a writer is inspiration—and that's what *Pop Prompts* gives you! The book is chock full of smart, engaging, clever writing prompts that seriously motivate you to get words on the page."
—Amber Benson, author of *The Witches of Echo Park*

"*Pop Prompts* is the book you've been waiting for. Erik will get you writing. He will pull that idea from you that you thought you'd lost forever."
—Liza Palmer, author of *Nowhere but Home*

"When I've looked at a draft so many times I want to puke, I turn to Erik's prompts. It never fails to breathe fresh life into my work."
—Ashley Quach, creator of *Deck the Halls (with Matrimony!)*

"Erik's prompts unlock my writerly brain like nothing else! They get those words flowing without fear—and ultimately drive me to uncover deeper truths about both my work and myself. Brilliant!"
—Sarah Kuhn, author of the *Heroine Complex* series

"Fun, engaging and surprising! Erik's way of teasing out the creative gems in you is masterful. This book is a resource I'll continue to utilize for a long, long time."
—Keiko Agena, author of *No Mistakes: A Perfect Workbook for Imperfect Artist*

SUNDAY SPRINTS

Interested in more writing prompts?

Need some motivation?

Do you work better when someone is holding you accountable?

Come to SUNDAY SPRINTS.

I host gently-guided writing sprints on Zoom every Wednesday from 6 to 8 p.m. PST and every Sunday from noon to 2 p.m. PST. (Yes, it's called Sunday Sprints on Wednesdays because . . . why not?)

Here's how it works: I give a new writing prompt every fifteen minutes. You write. That's it.

All sprinters stay on mute. Alone but not alone, you can draw creative energy from the community of writers on your screen. This is a fun, low-pressure environment—a safe space for you to experiment with your writing. No worries: I will never ask you to share your work.

You decide how to use this distraction-free writing time. Work on that screenplay, novel, short story, play, poem, song. Do some therapeutic journaling. Write letters to loved ones. Do some technical writing. Create a D&D campaign. Finish your homework. Seriously, whatever you need to work on.

Let's get that writing done. Together.

Join the Sunday Sprints Patreon at:
www.patreon.com/erikpatterson

Subscribe to the Sunday Sprints mailing list at:
www.erikpatterson.org.sundaysprints

Printed in Great Britain
by Amazon

24237738R00119